Poetry Street 1

compiled by
David Orme and James Sale

How to eat a Poem

Don't be polite.
Bite in.
Pick it up with your fingers and lick the juice that
    may run down your chin.
It is ready and ripe now, whenever you are.

You do not need a knife or fork or spoon
or plate or napkin or tablecloth.

For there is no core
or stem
or rind
or pit
or seed
or skin
to throw away.

EVE MERRIAM

How to use this book

We hope you will enjoy reading and listening to the poems in this book, and that you will enjoy the activities that go with them.

Reading the poems
Don't rush on to the activities until you have spent time enjoying the poems!

You should:

- listen to them read to you
- read them silently a number of times
- talk about them in class or small groups.

Poems use language in a very special way and your discussion will help you understand anything you find puzzling. Remember though, that no poem can be completely 'worked out' like a crossword puzzle. In good poems, there is always something new to be found and thought about every time you read them.

The activities
Many of the activities are designed to help you in your understanding of the poems in this book and of other poems you might read. Other activities suggest ideas for your own writing, for the best way to understand how writers work is to try it yourself! A number of the poems in the collection were written by poets still at school, and we have marked these with * in the Contents list.

David Orme and James Sale

Contents

About Us

1 Our imaginary worlds

The wind was on the withered heath,
but in the forest stirred no leaf:
there shadows lay by night and day,
and dark things silent crept beneath.

The wind came down from mountains cold,
and like a tide it roared and rolled;
the branches groaned, the forest moaned,
and leaves were laid upon the mould.

The wind went on from West to East;
all movement in the forest ceased,
but shrill and harsh across the marsh
its whistling voices were released.

The grasses hissed, their tassels bent,
the reeds were rattling – on it went
o'er shaken pool under heavens cool
where racing clouds were torn and rent.

It passed the lonely Mountain bare
and swept above the dragon's lair:
there black and dark lay boulders stark
and flying smoke was in the air.

It left the world and took it flight
over the wide seas of the night.
The moon set sail upon the gale,
and stars were fanned to leaping light.

J R R TOLKIEN

This poem has a regular pattern of:

- **RHYME**
  (What is it?)
- **LINE LENGTH**
  (count the syllables)
- and **RHYTHM**.

Read these two lines out loud, making the parts in capitals
LOUDER. What is the pattern of the rhythm?

> The WIND went ON from WEST to EAST
> all MOVEment IN the FOrest CEASED.

See if you can write an extra stanza* for the poem, describing the
effect of the wind when it reaches a city. Keep as close to the
pattern as you can.

* A stanza is a section of a poem divided from the other sections by
leaving a blank line. Sometimes these sections are called 'verses'.

Mixed-Up School

We have a crazy mixed-up school.
Our teacher Mrs Cheetah
Makes us talk backwards. Nicer cat
You wouldn't want to meet a.

To start the day we eat our lunch,
Then do some heavy dome-work.
The boys' and girls' rooms go to us,
The hamster marks our homework.

At recess time we race inside
To put on diving goggles,
Play pin-the-donkey-on-the-tail,
Ball-foot or ap-for-bobbles.

Old Cheetah, with a chunk of chalk,
Writes right across two blackbirds,
And when she says, 'Go home!' we walk
The whole way barefoot backwards.

X J KENNEDY

Here are some 'backward' words:
  BALL-FOOT
  AP-FOR-BOBBLES
Make up four more that could have been included in the poem.

Mrs Cheetah makes the pupils talk backwards. In the morning do they say
      CHEETAH MRS MORNING GOOD
   or DOOG GNINROM SRM HATEEHC
   or HATEEHC SRM GNINROM DOOG   ?
What do they say at the end of school?

Mirror poems

'You are old, Father William,'
the young man said.
'And your hair has become
very white;
And yet you incessantly
stand on your head,
Do you think, at your age,
it is right?'

'You are young, Mother Wendy,'
The old woman said,
'And your toes have become
very long;
And yet you never
stand on your own feet,
Do you think, my dear youth,
you are wrong?'

All mirrors will give you backwards, or 'mirror' writing. This mirror turns the poem backwards!
Find part of a poem from this book and try and turn it into a 'backwards' poem.

5

Sixteen steps to...

SIXTEEN steps to the ice-house
BLACK with slime-slither mould,
SIXTEEN steps to the dungeon depths
AND that petrifying cold
THAT holds the souls of servants
LIKE breath afraid to breathe
LEST it disturbs some sinewy shape –
NOT of this century.
CLATTER! as rat-scattered bones
SHATTER the stagnant still,
ECHO empty tunes to the dead
WHO guard, in ghostly chill,
SIXTEEN steps *from* the ice-house
BLACK with slime-slither mould,
SIXTEEN steps *from* the dungeon depths
AND that petrifying cold.

...the Ice-house

GINA DOUTHWAITE

Conversation with an Angel

On my way to Sainsbury's
I met an Angel. He stood
relaxed, one foot and one wing
off the pavement, waiting
for me to pass. I stopped
to see if he needed anything: had he
lost his way? Could I help perhaps?
No, he lacked nothing, simply wanted
some contact with the world again;
he'd been human once and he sometimes
craved that bitter-sweet flavour...
Some angels were born – he explained –
others translated. Could I
become an angel? Was there a waiting list?
Not a chance for you, he laughed,
no one who has seen
an angel can ever become one.

WANDA BARFORD

Choose one of these poems as a pattern for a poem of your own.

If you choose 'Conversation with an Angel', begin it
    On my way to Sainsbury's
    I met a ......?
'Sixteen steps to the Ice-house' could become 'Sixteen steps to the
Attic' or 'Sixteen steps to the Cellar', or...?

Sarah and Teddy

In the empty house Sarah took
Teddy in her arms. She forced
Mummy's lipstick to his stubborn
Cloth mouth then made him look
In the mirror; Teddy was shocked
But said nothing. Sarah slipped the black
Plastic lid from the pale cold cream,
Checked the bedroom door was locked
Then pressed the white softness hard down
Into Teddy's yielding fur. He
Grew limp yet slidy and shiny
As lino. Face powder hid his frown.

'That bear was bloody dear!' yelled Mummy
And slapped her daughter round the head.
'No tea for you until you've cleaned it
And then you'll go straight off to bed!'

In the bathroom Sarah clutched
Greasy Teddy in her arms.
Gently she lowered his bulk
Into the water
And kept him under.
'You're out of harm's
Way now. No need to sulk.'
Then, as an afterthought, 'I
Christen thee Mummy,' as bubbles
Rose to caress
The soft down of her arms.

JIM C WILSON

Teddy is a little shocked by Sarah's behaviour!

In pairs, improvise a conversation between Teddy and Sarah.
Teddy begins by asking Sarah 'Why are you pinching me?' Try and
turn your conversation into a short 'two person' play.

9

SCAFELL PIKE

Look
Along the well
Of the street,
Between the gasworks and the neat
Sparrow-stepped gable
Of the Catholic chapel,
High
Above tilt and crook
Of the tumbledown
Roofs of the town –
Scafell Pike,
The tallest hill in England.

How small it seems,
So far away,
No more than a notch
On the plate-glass window of the sky!
Watch
A puff of kitchen smoke
Block out peak and pinnacle –
Rock-pie of volcanic lava
Half a mile thick
Scotched out
At the click of an eye.

Look again
In five hundred, a thousand or ten
Thousand years:
A ruin where
The chapel was; brown
Rubble and scrub and cinders where

The gasworks used to be;
No roofs, no town,
Maybe no men;
But yonder where a lather-rinse of cloud pours down
The spiked wall of the sky-line, see,
Scafell Pike
Still there.

NORMAN NICHOLSON

Scafell Pike is the name of the highest mountain in England.

Read the poem carefully and talk about some of the unusual word
pictures in the poem. We have picked out some for you.

Above tilt and crook
Of the tumbledown
Roofs of the town –

No more than a notch
On the plate-glass window of the sky!

But yonder where a lather-rinse of cloud pours down
The spiked wall of the sky-line...

How will the place where you live look in five hundred years' time?
Is there anything that will remain the same? Will people have
disappeared altogether? Discuss in groups, or draw and write
about, what your area will be like in the twenty-fifth century.

2 Real worlds

The poems in the last section were all connected, in one way or another, with 'imaginary worlds'. Is 'The Bed' about a real world – or an imaginary one?

The Bed

'Don't crawl under the bed,' said his
mother.
'You don't know what lives under there.'
You see Jimmy had been messing around
with his bed
And she said it to give him a scare.

But Jimmy was only a youngster
And he had got it into his head
That there were terrible things that
lurked about
In the black depths under his bed.

And even as he grew older,
Dark and evil thoughts filled his mind,
and he never looked under the bed,
Too frightened of what he might find.

ADRIAN BOWDEN

This poem, written by Adrian Bowden when he was at school, won a competition for 'mystery' poems.

Make a class collection of 'mystery' poems for a display. You could turn it into a competition, if you like.

Is there a place that frightens you, especially at night? In groups, 'confess' your place of fear.

12

The Skateboard Boys

Choc. They slap up over
Concrete tablelands; they take
Their corners blind.
All around their country
Bangs with salvos:
Choc. Choc. And the accelerating
Lash of those tiny wheels.
They zizz in and out like
Fireworks or tracers in water
Going for silent heat.
All the ululations help them to hang
From skyscrapers so they can see
The sun from every possible angle;
Their ankles are as strong
As horses'; when they've had enough
They lean over the parapet
With spines like soft dolls.
The skateboard boys choc in and out
Past the drunks and the cardboard hostels:
At dusk they draw galaxies
With their firefly boards
In the crackling air.

HILARY DAVIES

Make a list of any unusual or difficult words in this poem and talk
about their meaning.

The title of this poem suggests only boys play with skateboards. Is
this true? You could try changing 'boy' for 'girl' in the poem – you
will need to change it once in the title and once in the poem itself.

Now write your own poem called 'The . . . . . . girls'. (You fill in the
missing word.)

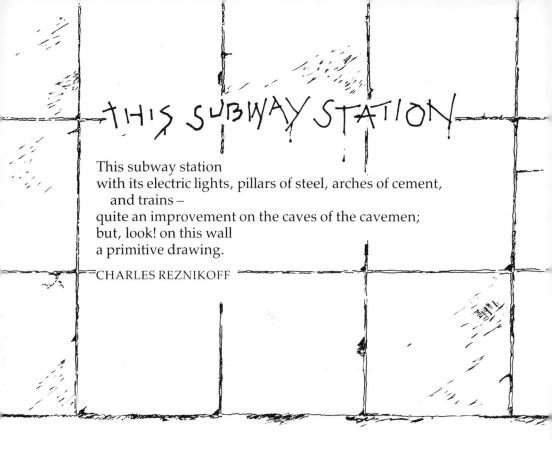

THIS SUBWAY STATION

This subway station
with its electric lights, pillars of steel, arches of cement,
   and trains –
quite an improvement on the caves of the cavemen;
but, look! on this wall
a primitive drawing.

CHARLES REZNIKOFF

Charles Reznikoff compares an underground station with cavemen's caves. In many ways they are different, but in one way they are the same; they both may have cave paintings!

In what ways might a big city resemble a tropical forest or African safari? See how many ideas you can add to this list:

CITY	TROPICAL FOREST
tall lampposts	giraffes
skyscrapers	tall trees
power cables	snakes and creepers
fast cars	?

At `Night` in the Laundrette

I sit in the laundrette
Watch my reflection sitting
On the chequered pavement

The black wet street reflects
Moonmilk, primroses
A bus sails by, a boat
Festooned with lanterns

My shadow warms itself
By a red puddle
Hell's fire flickers there
Stirred by drops of rain

GERDA MAYER

Travelling Man

I'm a travelling man, sir,
I'm a travelling man!
I've travelled round the world both ways
So you must listen to what I says
'Cos, I'm a travelling man!

I've
Been
To
Africa
Bermuda
China
Dakota
E...

I'm a travelling man, sir,
I'm a travelling man!
I've travelled in a bus and travelled in a van
I've travelled every way I can
'Cos I'm a travelling man!
I've
ridden
an
Antelope
a Bareback horse
a Clapped out car
a Dirty dustcart
a...

MANGO CHUTNEY

The author has left 'Travelling Man' unfinished. Can you finish it
for him?

Black Child

Black child sitting
on a sidewalk, sniffing.
Dream-cars slick past
out of touch, out of sight.

Black child stands,
hands in pocketless slacks,
and slouches off, away to play
in Hell's kitchen, all alone, and black.

K QUIGLEY

The poet writes:
*'I have tried to write with the rhythm of a black person's speech
– definitely musical, which is amazing when you see and hear
what they're up against!'*

Try reading out 'Black Child' in different ways, listening to its
rhythms.

3 Our friends

Oath of Friendship

Shang ya!

I want to be your friend
For ever and ever without break or decay.
When the hills are all flat
And the rivers are all dry,
When it lightens and thunders in winter,
When it rains and snows in summer,
When Heaven and Earth mingle –
Not till then will I part from you.

ANON, Chinese, 1st century BC (translated by Arthur Waley)

Oath of Friendship

I want to be friends with you till
the hens have run out of eggs,
the clouds have no rain in them
and I have no hair or tooth in my head.

If we are friends I will give you
a replica of the Mona Lisa,
Buckingham Palace complete with possessions and servants
and all the dentists' gold teeth in the world.

My friend I will like you more than
jam buns with cream oozing out,
watching television,
and sailing on the QE2 across the Atlantic Ocean.

HAYLEY YOUNG

Down at the Launderette

First time I ran away I was only eight.
St Stephens and Redgates had planned
a fight; I tagged along with the fourth years
marching in a gang, everyone dead hard
but the fight was off, the police came;
I didn't want to leave before the action
so I hung around to see what would happen.

It grew cold after dark; I shivered
with my hands stuck up the sleeves
of my jersey, too scared to go home.
The gang said they knew where to get warm,
took me to the launderette where
a woman was unloading her tumble drier.
'Climb in there quick; it's still hot.'

Then they shut the door, put money in,
just for the laugh. The attendant had
a key to unlock me but she threatened
to call the police if we didn't leave
so we moved off, me with grazed knees,
limping, laughing; they were saying
'He's a hard case, this kid, dead hard.'

IRENE RAWNSLEY

Sometimes we don't always choose very good friends!
After you have read Irene Rawnsley's poem, discuss in groups why
you think the character in the poem decided to 'tag along' with the
gang.

Now in your groups prepare a 'friend's charter'. List the things that
are most important in a friend. Try and put them in order of
importance.

I have a Friend

I have a friend called Ann
she crumples her Cola can.

I have a friend called Bruce
he spits in his orange juice.

I have a friend called Claire
she puts chewing gum in her hair.

I have a friend called Dennis
he knocks me out at tennis.

.   .   .   .   .   .

I have a friend called Xavier
he went to live in Belgravia.

I have a friend called Yvonne
her nickname is anon.

I have a friend called Zachariah
he lies, he's a great multiplier.

SUE STEWART

We have left out the central section of Sue Stewart's poem. Write
your own version of the missing stanzas.

Missing Person

All my life I've missed
the brother I never had.
I missed him at parties,
in the summer holidays,
the day our father died.

Isobel had George, gruff
in white tennis shorts,
nodding at us girls. Nita
had Jim, Sheena, Robin.
Rude, dismissive, but there.

I knew all about him, this
brother of mine, name, age,
two years older than me. He
walked with me in the deep
trenches of the night.

I wanted that brother like
I cried for the moon. I must
have been a pest, always on
about it. Maybe I stepped on a
sore point between my parents.

You don't think about things
like that. Maybe they wanted
a son. Grown-up, I see Muriel
with her brother, mourn mine
like a death in the family.

MOIRA ANDREW

Most people have 'imaginary friends' at some time or another.
They have some advantages over real friends; what are they?
Moira Andrew had an imaginary brother. Why do you think the
brother was so important to her? Why might she have 'stepped on
a sore point between her parents'?

'I had a secret'

I had a secret
and told it
to my best friend.

She told her second best friend
who told *her* best friend
and no one else.

No one else
told somebody else
who told anyone
who told her best friend.

Now everyone knows
my secret
so it's not a secret
any more. Now
it's news.

SUE STEWART

When you made your 'friend's charter' did you include 'able to keep a secret' on it?

When secrets are passed from one person to another, they often change as each person exaggerates the story a little. Make up a secret. Write it as the first stanza of a poem.
In the second stanza, a 'friend' passes the secret on to someone else – but the story changes!
In the third stanza, the new person passes the story on again. How has it changed this time?

Your poem can be as long as you wish.

Why won't she Listen?

My friend Mandy's fat but even
that's not her biggest problem
which is, she doesn't even care.

She's fat and plain from her
smooth round face with little
brown eyes to her podgy feet in
flat, battered shoes, size eights.

She won't put on make-up or spend
time on what she wears. I've never
even seen her glance into a mirror
checking on her hair. She won't diet
or come to Mum's gym with me to
work-out, do some re-structuring.
She is a *mess*. I tell her straight.

When I said I'd give her streaks
or do a perm she only grinned.
And said what she always says
that she's satisfied with being
the way she is. But she *can't* be!

I watch her when we're waiting for
the teacher in the morning. We all
stand round Mandy's chair to talk.
It's a shame! Poor Mandy, bulging
through the chair. She *should* care.

I do wish she'd listen, take my
advice. I really could help, offered
twice today but as usual didn't have
chance to say what I wanted to –

24

with people trying to get her to
agree to play chess, or talking
about soccer and other rubbish –
like a boring book they've all read.

If I go after school she's never
alone – she's a pretty good cook
has a darkroom at home. There's some
sort of camera club meets every month.
But I never go. They're all so boring!

JOAN POULSON

Discuss this poem in small groups.

What do you think of Mandy?
What do you think of the person telling the story of the poem?
Which person would you rather be?

Friend

'Please, Sir, we get bored with writing:
Can't we do something more exciting?'

'Writing's fine,' he said,
'if you choose something good to write about.
I have a suggestion:
Let's write about our friends.
Now then: what is a friend?
Try to answer that question,
try to think it out.
Think about it in your head
before you start writing.'

I sat there a bit, chewing the end
of a pencil. Opened my book
And glared at all the empty pages.
Found a hanky and cleaned my glasses.
Found a bit of chocolate in my coat.
Ate it. Nothing else to do.
I hate English classes.

'You there!' he yelled, 'You!
What are you doing?
Are you chewing?'
'Who, me, Sir? No, not me.'
Picked up my pen. Wrote:

MY BEST FRIEND
My best friend is Peter Evans in 3C.
He lives at the end of the lane, right by the brook.
I've known him for ages.
He's always acting the fool
in lessons. He's no good at spellings and all that stuff,
but he doesn't care.
He plays in goal for the school.

What's he like, though?
What does he look like?
Well, he's not as tall as me;
he's got freckles and brown hair;
he's scruffy
– you know.
He rides a bike.
My Mum doesn't like him.
I know she doesn't like him.
Whenever there's a fight or something like that,
or someone's been bunging rubble
at someone's window, or shooting someone's cat
with an airgun, or tying bits of string
across the footpath, that sort of thing,
it's always Peter and me who get the blame,
always! They always blame us.

That's why Mum doesn't like him; because
she says he gets me a bad name.
She says he leads me into trouble.
Funny thing, though,
what she doesn't know:
Peter's Mum says just the same.

I don't think she likes me much, Peter's mother.

That's what it is, see,
having friends: taking the blame for each other;
getting punished and not caring;
lying in the long grass in Summer, sharing
silences; having fights and falling out.

Oh, God! This is a stupid thing to have to write about!

I get really bored with stupid writing,
specially when it's stupid titles like 'My Best Friend'.
I wish we could do something more exciting.

Pick up my pen again.
Write: THE END

TONY CHARLES

Describing people is not always easy. Most people write a list of things, like the character in Tony Charles's poem starts to do. He soon gets stuck!

It is much more interesting to describe people by writing about some of the things they have done that tell us something about the sort of person they are. If the character in the poem had written down what was in his head, the teacher would probably have been delighted!

Try a piece of writing about a person you know well. Include stories of things they have done as well as a 'description' of them.

4 Ourselves: using 'I'

First Day at School

A millionbillionwillion miles from home
Waiting for the bell to go. (To go where?)
Why are they all so big, other children?
So noisy? So much at home they
must have been born in uniform
Lived all their lives in playgrounds
Spent the years inventing games
that don't let me in. Games
that are rough, that swallow you up.

And the railings.
All around, the railings.
Are they to keep out wolves and monsters?
Things that carry off and eat children?
Things you don't take sweets from?
Perhaps they're to stop us getting out
Running away from the lessins. Lessin.
What does a lessin look like?
Sounds small and slimy.
They keep them in glassrooms.
Whole rooms made out of glass. Imagine.

I wish I could remember my name
Mummy said it would come in useful.
Like wellies. When there's puddles.
Lellowwellies. I wish she was here.
I think my name is sewn on somewhere
Perhaps the teacher will read it for me.
Tea-cher. The one who makes the tea.

ROGER MCGOUGH

Script

Miss Coleman held up flashcards and we'd yell:
Yes! Good! House! Cat! Bell!

We practised our loops and joins with dip pens
in the staves of the buff exercise books.

My end of term report said: writing poor.
My fingers wore ink gloves. The letters hunched
in corners, mobbed each other, fell off lines.

Others, abandoning both page and pen,
patiently carved their names into the desk
or with a chalk (we had no spray cans then)
wrote 'Bum' unevenly up on some wall.

At breakfast I read the Kellogg's packet.
On the bus I read my orange ticket.
At school I read 'In case of fire break glass'.

I was given a fountain pen but ate it.
The report said: English good, writing poor.

Waiting for the bus I read the shop signs:
Coal Order Office was my favourite.

My parents' faces were lined and silent
as closed, densely written exercise books.
The ruels were changing all the time and I
was lost. The report said: spelling still poor.

My father smashed the breakfast things one day.
My mother never forgave him for it.
The china fragments lay like bits of words

all through the dining room. My sister hid
and locked her door. He's mad, my mother said,
raving mad. I read the cornflakes packet:
thyamin, nyacin, riboflavin,
and Mr Kellogg's signature in special script.
And no one spoke, explained, apologised,
forgave or understood – or even cared.

My end of term report said: writing worse.

STEPHEN JENKINS

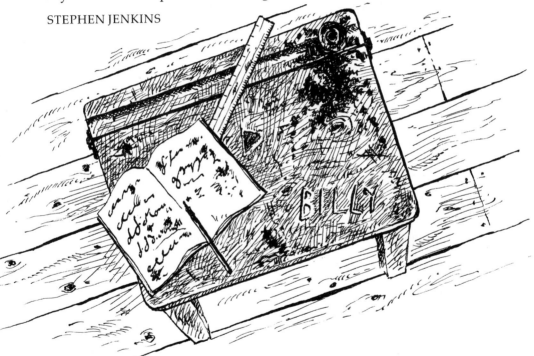

Reminiscing

How far back can you remember your school life? Talk about your
earliest school memories, using a tape recorder if one is available.
Pick two or three of the 'reminiscences' and write them out for a
display. (A written out copy of a tape is called a 'transcript'.)

SWOT

They pinch my bag
rip the strap off
stuff it with Stink Horn
leave it in the shower

throw pumps at me
call me 'Crab Eyes'
tie my legs together
roll me down the bank

I told the form master once
They took my rough book
wrote GRASS all over
in green felt tip

It's not my fault
I'm good at maths
and don't like
a hard ball

I know I'm rather
absentminded
and sometimes
don't hear the bell

I know I'm
a bit eccentric
and sometimes
chatter on like a kid

but when I'm happy
my time's not theirs
but the kind
clouds have in the summer

I'd like to leave
live on an island
scoff melons
and coconut scoop

do calculus
with my feet up
ride elephant turtles
down to the sea

GEOFFREY HOLLOWAY

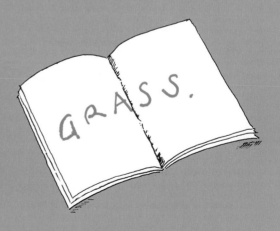

My Parents Kept Me

My parents kept me from children who were rough
Who threw words like stones and who wore torn clothes.
Their thighs showed through rags. They ran in the street
And climbed cliffs and stripped by the country streams.

I feared more than tigers their muscles like iron
Their jerking hands and their knees tight on my arms.

I feared the salt coarse pointing of those boys
Who copied my lisp behind me on the road.

They were lithe, they sprang out behind hedges
Like dogs to bark at my world. They threw mud
While I looked the other way, pretending to smile.
I longed to forgive them, but they never smiled.

STEPHEN SPENDER

Both of these poems are about people that don't 'fit in'. Stephen
Spender as a child was rejected because he was too well off; why
was Geoffrey Holloway treated so badly?

Now improvise a five-minute play called 'The Outcast'.

Dumb Insolence

I'm big for ten years old
Maybe that's why they get at me

Teachers, parents, cops
Always getting at me

When they get at me

I don't hit em
They can do you for that

I don't swear at em
They can do you for that

I think about sick

They call it dumb insolence

They don't like it
But they can't do you for it

ADRIAN MITCHELL

In this poem Adrian Mitchell PRETENDS to be a ten year old, and writes in the PRESENT TENSE, as if what he is telling us about is happening NOW.

I'm big...
I think about sick

If Adrian Mitchell was writing about his own childhood, like Stephen Spender, the first two lines might be:

I was big for ten years old
May be that's why they got at me

Rewrite the rest of the poem as if the poet was writing about the past.

Look through all the poems in this section. Which ones are 'reminiscences' and which ones pretend to be written by a young person?

About Poets

Judith Nicholls

Judith Nicholls introduces
her own selection of poems
by herself and her choice of
poems by other poets.

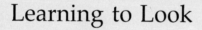

Learning to Look

No one needs to be a genius in order to find something to write about! We all have enough experiences, feelings, memories to produce several books of poetry – but often we just don't look at those experiences carefully enough. In each of these poems I have tried to look more closely at something in my own life.

Unfortunately, it's not quite enough just to look and then pour out all the ideas on to paper. This is all right for a personal diary but it won't work for a poem! A poem has to be made and the ideas shaped and worked upon, over and over again if necessary.

JUDITH NICHOLLS

The Dare

Go on, I dare you,
come on down!

Was it *me* they called?
Pretend you haven't heard,
a voice commanded in my mind.
Walk past, walk fast
and don't look down,
don't look behind.

Come on, it's easy!

The banks were steep,
the water low
and flanked with oozing brown.
Easy? Walk fast
but don't look down.
Walk straight, walk on,
even risk their jeers
and run . . .

Never go near those dykes,
my mother said.
No need to tell me.
I'd seen stones sucked in
and covered without trace,
gulls slide to bobbing safety,
grasses drown as water rose.
No need to tell me
to avoid the place.

She ca-a-a-n't, she ca-a-a-n't!

Cowardy, cowardy custard!

There's no such word as 'can't',
my father said.
I slowed my pace.
The voice stopped,
waited as I wavered, grasping breath.
My mother's wrath? My father's scorn?
A watery death?

I hesitated then turned back,
forced myself to see the mud below.
After all, it was a dare . . .
There was no choice;
I had to go.

JUDITH NICHOLLS

Dare Cinquains

1
Steep banks
and oozing mud
are all I see below;
no friends, just voices jeering: 'Yes –
or no?'

2
Go on,
I dare you, jump!
Mud lapped with water swims
before my eyes; behind, in dreams
I drown.

JUDITH NICHOLLS

Turn 'The Dare' into a short play. Here are some ideas and things to think about.

1 Decide how many characters you will need.

2 Most of the words are in the main character's head. How are you going to deal with this?
(How do television programmes get over this problem? If you don't know, find out what a 'voice-over' is.)

3 Where will you end your play? If you wish to carry the story on, you could do so in mime, or you could write further stanzas. Is there a rhyming pattern to the stanzas?

Has a similar situation happened to you? Write about it in a story, poem or short play. Find out how speech is set out in playwriting.

Then

They never expected it of my grandmother,
all this choice.
Stolid, vocationally-trained
with neat samplers and clear instructions on
pastry-making and how to preserve the strawberries,
for forty years she happily baked my grandfather
rabbit pie, brawn, haslet;
collected fresh farm milk,
still-twitching pullets
and their warm muck-splattered eggs,
manure for the rhubarb, and mushrooms
dawn-gathered in chill Lincolnshire fields.

JUDITH NICHOLLS

Judith Nicholls writes:
*I wanted to write about my grandmother in some way because
her life seemed so different from mine. Sometimes we can write
about people by describing their appearance, the way they
behave, the things they say. In 'Then' I chose to write about
her by picking out instead some of the things in her life – the
food she cooked, the eggs she collected from my uncle's farm,
the mushrooms she gathered . . .*

Read carefully what Judith Nicholls says about writing about
people. Just describing their appearance doesn't tell us much
about them. A better way is to write about things that are – or were
– important in their lives.

Try this now in a piece of writing about an adult you remember
well.

Haiku

There are thanks to be given:
    this snow on the bed quilt –
      it too is from Heaven.

ISSA
(translated from the Japanese by
Harold G Henderson)

Hello there, old stumbling-block!

    keep up your irritating,
    for the pearl I am making.

LIBBY HOUSTON

Cinquains are poems with a strict pattern. Look closely at the two
by Judith Nicholls to find out what the pattern is, then try one of
your own. Remember what Judith Nicholls says about working on
your writing until it is just right; you may have to rewrite your
cinquain several times until it is right.

The poem by Issa is a HAIKU: you will find out more about these
very short poems on page 74. Libby Houston's poem is very short,
too; there are only fourteen words in it. You have to work really
hard with poems as short as this; there are no words to spare!

41

LINES

I must never daydream in schooltime.
I just love a daydream in Mayshine.
I must ever greydream in timeschool.
Why must others paydream in schoolway?
Just over highschool dismay lay.
Thrust over skydreams in cryschool.
Cry dust over drydreams in screamtime.
Dreamschool thirst first in dismayday.
Why lie for greyday in crimedream?
My time for dreamday is soontime.
In soontime must I daydream ever.
Never must I say dream in strifetime.
Cry dust over daydreams of lifetimes.
I must never daydream in schooltime.
In time I must daydream never.

JUDITH NICHOLLS

OPENING THE CAGE *14 variations on 14 words*

I have nothing to say and I am saying it and that is poetry.

JOHN CAGE

I have to say poetry and is that nothing and am I saying it
I am and I have poetry to say and is that nothing saying it
I am nothing and I have poetry to say and that is saying it
I that am saying poetry have nothing and it is I and to say
And I say that I am to have poetry and saying it is nothing
I am poetry and nothing and saying it is to say that I have
To have nothing is poetry and I am saying that and I say it
Poetry is saying I have nothing and I am to say that and it
Saying nothing I am poetry and I have to say that and it is
It is and I am and I have poetry saying say that to nothing
It is saying poetry to nothing and I say I have and am that
Poetry is saying I have it and I am nothing and to say that
And that nothing is poetry I am saying and I have to say it
Saying poetry is nothing and to that I say I am and have it

EDWIN MORGAN

42

'Lines' is a very tricky poem to read out loud; try it!

Now try it with *fifteen* people reading a line each. You will need to practise it first!

Do you think this poem is just about playing with words, or does Judith Nicholls have something to say about school life?

Now try to read 'Opening the Cage' with *fourteen* people reading a line each. Is this just a word pattern? Is Edwin Morgan saying something about poetry?

Judith Nicholls makes up some new words in 'Lines'; here are some of them:

GREYDREAM	SCHOOLWAY	GREYDAY
SKYDREAMS	SCREAMTIME	CRIMEDREAM

They are made up by joining two words together. Choose two of these 'doublewords' from the poem and make up dictionary definitions for them. Make up some 'doublewords' of your own.

Judith Nicholls writes:

'Lines' is a poem I specially enjoyed working on – but it took several days to write! It began with a simple idea: someone is given lines to do as a punishment for daydreaming and as the lines are being written the daydreaming takes over again! There were plenty of obvious possibilities for word mix-ups (ever/never, daydream/greydream, must/dust etc.). However, I couldn't just 'mix and hope'! Even invented words like greydream *and* drydream *seem to suggest particular meanings or feelings – I needed to be sure the poem would sound and feel as I wanted.*

Edwin Morgan's 'Opening the Cage' is of course another variation on playing with words and this partly gave me the idea for 'Lines', which I took a step further by breaking words in two and making new ones. These new words, I hoped, would expand my meaning further.

Fishing Song

Ragworm, lugworm, mackerel, maggot,
Grey pike lurking, still as steel.
Cast my rod in the deep dark stream
With a nugget of bread for a silver bream.

                                          Caught an eel.

Ragworm, lugworm, mackerel, maggot,
Number Ten hook and I'm waiting still.
A carp would be good or a spiny perch,
A golden rudd or a red-finned roach?

                                          It's an eel.

Ragworm, lugworm, mackerel, maggot,
Something's biting, wind up the reel!
Is it a pike or a roach or a rudd?
A hunting gudgeon from the river bed?

                                          Just – an eel.

JUDITH NICHOLLS

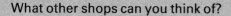

Ragworm, lugworm, mackerel, maggot...

Judith Nicholls 'found' this list outside a fish shop.

Write a list of four things you might find advertised outside

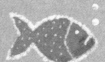

- a greengrocer's shop
- a butcher's shop
- a sweet shop
- a supermarket.

What other shops can you think of?

Say Judith Nicholls' line about the fish over and over until you hear its rhythm. Make the same rhythm with the list of things you have chosen. You may have to change some of the items to fit the rhythm!

Put all your lists together and perform your 'High Street' poem.

Learning to Swim

Today I am
dolphin-over-the-waves,
roach and stickleback,
silver mermaid,
turning tide,
ribbon-weed
or sprat.

Water drifts through my mind;
I twist, I glide,
leave fear behind in sand,
wander a land
of turtle, minnow, seal
where whale is king.

Today – I swim!

JUDITH NICHOLLS

Wish for a Young Wife

My lizard, my lively writher,
May your limbs never wither,
May the eyes in your face
Survive the green ice
Of envy's mean gaze;
May you live out your life
Without hate, without grief,
And your hair ever blaze,
In the sun, in the sun,
When I am undone,
When I am no one.

THEODORE ROETHKE

RHYME is sometimes a problem when you are writing poetry. Rhyme makes poetry more musical and memorable, but sometimes it is difficult to choose a good rhyme that also says exactly what you mean.

Find the rhymes in 'Learning to Swim' and 'Wish for a Young Wife'. Are there any rhyme patterns in these poems?

Now look at these pairs of words:

MIND	SAND
FACE	ICE
TIDE	GLIDE
LIFE	GRIEF
STICKLEBACK	SPRAT
WRITHER	WITHER
SWIM	KING

Which ones rhyme? Which ones don't?

Some of them almost rhyme, or have similar sounds. Which ones?

When words nearly rhyme we get 'near-rhymes'.

Judith Nicholls writes:
Theodore Roethke is one of my favourite poets. In 'Wish for a Young Wife', he plays with words until he has the maximum out of them. One of the lessons I learned here is that rhyme doesn't have to be 'exact' – an echoing near-rhyme *can sometimes be even more effective. I tried one or two of these in 'Learning to Swim'.* Tide *and* glide *were straightforward...but I could add a further echo with* weed; sand *and* land *clearly rhymed...but I wanted to say 'Water drifts through my* mind' *and this was not only all right, but* mind *would add to my sound pattern too. Nor was there any need to restrict my echoes to the ends of lines only: I could use* Just *and* Thrust *(in 'Lines') at the start of two successive lines, or* ever *and* Never *at the end of one and beginning of the next.... The 'rules' were there to be used – or broken!*

Partners

Find a partner,
says sir, and sit
with him or her.
A whisper here,
a shuffle there,
a rush of feet.
One pair,
another pair,
till twenty-four
sit safely on the floor
and all are gone
but one
who stands,
like stone,
and waits;
tall,
still,

alone.

JUDITH NICHOLLS

Judith Nicholls writes:
'Partners' is about one of my least favourite memories of school
– a PE lesson on a day when a best friend is away. You'll see
that this is a long, thin poem. The last three words have each
been given a line to themselves, to slow down the reading,
to show how alone I was feeling.

40 – love

middle	aged
couple	playing
ten-	nis
when	the
game	ends
and	they
go	home
the	net
will	still
be	be-
tween	them

ROGER MCGOUGH

Judith Nicholls writes:

There is no wastage of words in Roger McGough's poem; I am impressed by just how much is said by the space down the middle and the title alone!

To put over all the ideas here in prose would have required far more words. '40 – love' was one of the early poems that sent me running back to my own efforts to remove inessential words which weren't really working for their keep.

Read 'Partners' again. Now retell it as a prose story. How many words do you need?

You could use the idea in Roger McGough's poem to write a 'sport' poem of your own. Ideas might be:

- the goalkeeper's great save
- table tennis.

How would a rounders poem be set out?

ADVICE

Do put a coat on,
and fasten that shoe.
I'd take a sweater,
    if I were you...

It's chilly at nights now,
you're bound to catch 'flu;
I'd button up warmly,
    if I were you...

Please yourself if you must
but I know what *I'd* do;
I'd stay at home now,
    if I were you...

The nights have drawn in,
you never know who
might be lurking out there
    just waiting for you...

I don't know what the youth
of today's coming to!
They do what they like
    and like what they do!

Now when *I* was young,
it caused hullaballoo
if I stayed out past nine –
    and I never dared to.

If I were young now,
I know what *I'd* do...
    I'd enjoy every minute
    if I were you!

JUDITH NICHOLLS

50

Ballad of the Faithless Wife

Carry her down to the river
  Carry her down to the sea
Let the bully-boys stare at her braided hair
  But never a glance from me.

Down by the writhing water
  Down by the innocent sand
They laid my bride by the toiling tide
  A stone in her rifled hand.

Under the dainty eagle
  Under the ravening dove
Under a high and healthy sky
  I waited for my love.

Off she ran with a soldier
  Tall as a summer tree,
Soft as a mouse he came to my house
  And stole my love from me.

O splintered were all the windows
  And broken all the chairs
War like a knife ran through my life
  And the blood ran down the stairs.

Loud on the singing morning
  I hear the mad birds rise
Safe from harm to the sun's alarm
  As the sound of fighting dies.

I would hang my harp on the branches
  And weep all through the day
But stranger, see! The wounded tree
  Has burned itself away.

False O false was my lover
  Dead on the diamond shore
White as a fleece, for her name was Peace
  And the soldier's name was War.

CHARLES CAUSLEY

52

if i have made, my lady, intricate
imperfect various things chiefly which wrong
your eyes (frailer than most deep dreams are frail)
songs less firm than your body's whitest song
upon my mind—if i have failed to snare
the glance too shy—if through my singing slips
the very skillful strangeness of your smile
the keen primeval silence of your hair

—let the world say 'his most wise music stole
nothing from death'—
                                            you only will create
(who are so perfectly alive) my shame:
lady through whose profound and fragile lips
the sweet small clumsy feet of April came

into the ragged meadow of my soul.

e e cummings

o every thing there is a season,
and a time to every purpose under
the heaven:
A time to be born, and a time to
die; a time to plant, and a time
to pluck up that which is planted;
A time to kill, and a time to heal;
a time to break down, and a time to
build up;
A time to weep, and a time to laugh;
a time to mourn, and a time to dance;
A time to cast away stones, and a
time to gather stones together; a
time to embrace, and a time to
refrain from embracing;
A time to get, and a time to lose;
a time to keep, and a time to cast away;
A time to rend, and a time to sew;
a time to keep silence, and a time
to speak;
A time to love, and a time to hate;
a time of war, and a time of peace.

BOOK OF ECCLESIASTES, Chapter 3, 1–8

Is the Bible extract a poem? What *is* a poem?
Discuss these difficult questions in groups.
Look for 'poetry patterns' in the poems 'Advice' and 'Ballad of the Faithless Wife'.

> ### Judith Nicholls writes:
> *There are plenty of things a poet must think about before a poem can be completed. Whilst no one needs to be a genius to find something to write about, most of us certainly need to take time to work at writing it!*

About Poems

1 Poems that tell stories

The Bunyip and the Whistling Kettle

I knew a most superior camper
    Whose methods were absurdly wrong,
He did not live on tea and damper
    But took a little stove along.

And every place he came to settle
    He spread with gadgets saving toil,
He even had a whistling kettle
    To warn him it was on the boil.

Beneath the waratahs and wattles,
    Boronia and coolibah,
He scattered paper, cans and bottles,
    And parked his nasty little car.

He camped, this sacrilegious stranger
    (The moon was at the full that week),
Once in a spot that teemed with danger
    Beside a bunyip-haunted creek.

He spread his junk but did not plunder,
    Hoping to stay the weekend long;
He watched the bloodshot sun go under
    Across the silent billabong.

He ate canned food without demurring,
    He put the kettle on for tea.
He did not see the water stirring
    Far out beside a sunken tree.

Then, for the day had made him swelter
    And night was hot and tense to spring,
He donned a bathing-suit in shelter
    And left the firelight's friendly ring.

He felt the water kiss and tingle.
    He heard the silence—none too soon!
A ripple broke against the shingle,
    And dark with blood it met the moon.

Abandoned in the hush, the kettle
    Screamed as it guessed its master's plight,
And loud it screamed, the lifeless metal,
    Far into the malicious night.

JOHN MANIFOLD

There are some unusual words in this Australian poem:

DAMPER
WARATAHS and WATTLES
BUNYIP
BILLABONG

If you are not sure of the meaning of them, make up suitable meanings of your own.

What does John Manifold feel about the camper? Write down a list of all the words in the poem that help you find this out.

Redback on the Toilet Seat

There was a redback on the toilet seat
When I was there last night.
I didn't see him in the dark,
But boy I felt his bite.

I jumped high up into the air
And when I hit the ground,
That crafty redback spider
Wasn't nowhere to be found.

I rushed in to the Missus,
Told her just where I'd been bit.
She grabbed a cut-throat razor-blade
And I nearly took a fit.

I said, 'Just forget what's on your mind
And call a doctor please,
Cause I got a feeling that your cure
Is worse than the disease.'

There was a redback on the toilet seat
When I was there last night.
I didn't see him in the dark,
But boy I felt his bite.

And now I'm here in hospital
A sad and sorry sight,
And I curse the redback spider
On the toilet seat last night.

I can't lie down, I can't sit up
And I don't know what to do,
And all the nurses think it's funny
But that's not my point of view.

I tell you it's embarrassing,
And that's to say the least,
That I'm too sick to eat a bite
While that spider had a feast.

And when I get back home again
I tell you what I'll do,
I'll make that redback suffer
For the pain I'm going through.

I've had so many needles
That I'm looking like a sieve,
And I promise you that spider
Hasn't very long to live.

There was a redback on the toilet seat
When I was there last night.
I didn't see him in the dark,
But boy I felt his bite.

But now I'm here in hospital
A sad and sorry sight,
And I curse the redback spider
On the toilet seat last night.

SLIM NEWTON
(reproduced with permission of Yeldah Music, Australia)

This is a good poem to perform, perhaps to the school or another class. You will need to read it with a suitable expression on your face!

A poetry performance always goes well if you can learn the poem by heart. This would not be too difficult if you shared the poem in a group – one or two stanzas each.

You discussed places that frighten you earlier in this book. Now write a paragraph describing the CREATURES you fear. What is it about them you particularly dislike?

The Troll

A troll once lived in a high pasture,
(A troll, a troll wife and their children too)
And one day there came a bold farmer
To speak with the troll as farmers do.

'Let us', he said, 'a bargain complete'
(A troll, a troll wife and their children too)
'I'll till this land, and what grows beneath
(This year I suggest a crop of wheat)
Shall be yours, Sir Troll, for this barren heath
Bears nothing that you can burn or eat.'
The troll, his troll wife and their children too
Were well enough pleased for the roots gave heat.

But the troll said 'Next year what's above ground
Shall be mine'; so the farmer turnips planted
And the trolls an excellent salad made
Of the turnip leaves. But the farmer haunted

By his new found wealth and his old found greed,
(A troll, a troll wife and their children too)
A village with barns and a small church made
Where the church bells rang by night and day
And the troll, cursed out by the horrible sound,
With his family sadly trailed away.

Come summer and the farmer a feast prepared,
Rich, for his sole daughter was to be wed
But far on the heath an idiot boy
Met with the troll and the troll king said,

'This parcel, my son, be pleased to carry'
(A troll, a troll wife and their children too)
'It's a present for Farmer Will and his heir.'
It was icy cold and as lead heavy,
But the boy took it to the wedding pair.

And the parcel contained a lake, a lake
(A troll, a troll wife and their children too)
And it drowned all the company drinking there
Except for the boy who could swim like a swan
For a bargain was at stake, at stake
With a troll, a troll wife and their children.

THOMAS BLACKBURN

These cartoon pictures tell the story of the Troll, but they are in the
wrong order. Work out the correct order of the pictures. We have
added one picture that does not fit the story at all; which one is it?
Use the 'extra' picture to start your own story.

The Hound of Ulster

Little boy
Will you stop
And take a look
In the puppy shop—
Dogs blue and liver
Noses aquiver
Little dogs big dogs
Dogs for sport and pleasure
Fat dogs meagre dogs
Dogs for lap and leisure.
Do you see that wire-haired terrier?
Could anything be merrier?
Do you see that Labrador retriever?
His name is Belvoir.
    Thank you courteous stranger, said the child.
    By your words I am beguiled.
    But tell me I pray
    What lurks in the gray
    Cold shadows at the back of the shop?
Little boy do not stop
Come away
From the puppy shop.
For the Hound of Ulster lies tethered there
Cuchulain tethered by his golden hair
His eyes are closed and his lips are pale
Hurry little boy he is not for sale.

STEVIE SMITH

How would you pronounce 'Belvoir'? The poem tells you the answer!

Stevie Smith's poem will make the start of an unusual story of your own, in poetry or prose. You might imagine why Cuchulain is tied

up at the back of the shop, or what happens when the boy doesn't do what he is told and buys the 'Hound of Ulster'.

You might be able to find the story of 'The Hound of Ulster' in your library.

The Great Panjandrum

So she went into the garden
to cut a cabbage-leaf
to make an apple-pie;
and at the same time
a great she-bear, coming down the street,
pops its head into the shop.
What! no soap?
        So he died,
and she very imprudently married the Barber:
and there were present
the Picaninnies,
      and the Joblillies,
       and the Garyulies,
and the great Panjandrum himself,
with the little round button at top;
and they all fell to playing the game of catch-as-catch-can,
till the gunpowder ran out at the heels of their boots.

SAMUEL FOOTE

Stories usually make some sort of sense – but not always! Can you write a poem as nonsensical as this?

You can make up new words of your own (such as 'Joblillies').

You may have heard of a famous poem called 'Jabberwocky' by Lewis Carroll. This is written almost entirely in made up words. See if you can find a copy of this poem.

Quick on the Draw

He was so quickonthedraw
He fired twice
Had a haircut
A drink in the saloon
And rode out of town
Before the sheriff's hand
Hit the holster.

ROGER MCGOUGH

Most of the poems in this section have been quite long, because
stories take some time to tell. 'Quick on the Draw' is over very
quickly – in more ways that one!

How short a story can you write?
- less than 50 words?
- less than 25?
- less than 10?

('Quick on the Draw' has 27 words.)

Freeze

The windowsill has grown a beard

      c   c
      i   i
      c   c
      l   l
      e   e

Milk bottles raise their ^{caps}

While puddles cr$_a$ck like broken glass

And trees wear furry w^{rap}s.

SUSAN COWLING

In Susan Cowling's poem the words on the page start to form the *shapes* of the things described.

Choose another type of weather for your own poem.

Just a Passing Shower

sunshine	sunshine	sunshine
sunshine	sunshine	//////////
sunshine	//////////	sunshine
//////////	sunshine	sunshine
sunshine	sunshine	sunshine

ALAN RIDDELL

In what ways is this poem like 'Freeze'? How would you make one about a cloudy day with passing snow showers?

Cardinal Ideograms

0   A mouth. Can blow or breathe,
be funnel, or Hello.

1   A grass blade or a cut.

2   A question seated. And a proud
bird's neck.

3   Shallow mitten for two-fingered hand.

4   Three-cornered hut
on one stilt. Sometimes built
so the roof gapes.

5   A policeman. Polite.
Wearing visored cap.

6   O unrolling,
tape of ambiguous length
on which is written the mystery
of everything curly.

7   A step,
detached from its stair.

8

The universe in diagram:
A cosmic hourglass.
(Note enigmatic shape,
absence of any valve of origin,
how end overlaps beginning.)
Unknotted like a shoelace
and whipped back and forth,
can serve as a model of time.

9

Lorgnette for the right eye.
In England or if you are Alice
the stem is on the left.

10

A grass blade or a cut
companioned by a mouth.
Open? Open. Shut? Shut.

MAY SWENSON

May Swenson has been looking closely at the shapes of the
cardinal numbers. Try to write ideograms for some of these
letters:

A   S

C   T

H   V

J   X

P

Q

The Good Taste Estate

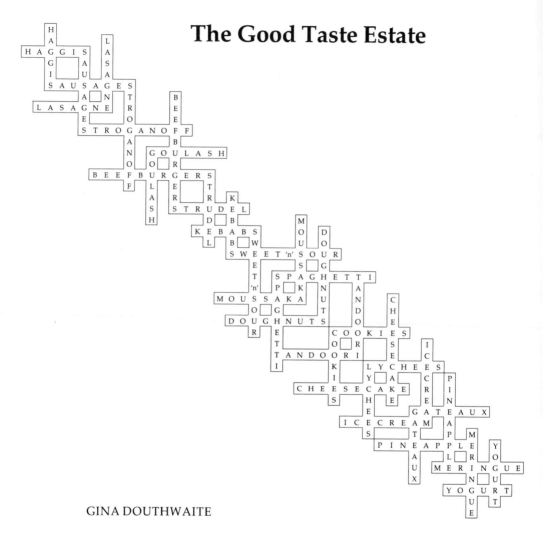

GINA DOUTHWAITE

Look carefully at the pattern of Gina Douthwaite's 'The Good Taste
Estate' before you try your own version. Here are some ideas:
   'The Bad Taste Estate'
   'The Animal's Estate'
   'The School Estate'

70

'It *is* a long tail, certainly,' said Alice, looking down with
wonder at the Mouse's tail; 'but why do you call it sad?' And
she kept on puzzling about it while the Mouse was speaking,
so that her idea of the tale was something like this:–

'Fury said to
a mouse, That
he met in the
house, 'Let
us both go
to law : *I*
will prose-
cute *you*. —
Come, I'll
take no de-
nial : We
must have
the trial;
For really
this morn-
ing I've
nothing
to do.'
Said the
mouse to
the cur,
'Such a
trial, dear
sir, With
no jury
or judge,
would
be wast-
ing our
breath.'
'I'll be
judge,
I'll be
jury,'
said
cun-
ning
old
Fury:
'I'll
try
the
whole
cause,
and
con-
demn
you to
death.'"

LEWIS CARROLL

Here are two possible titles for
Lewis Carroll's poem:

A MOUSE'S TAIL
A MOUSE'S TALE

Which would you choose?

A reading of this poem needs to
become quieter and quieter. Try
reading it by starting with the
whole class and gradually
dropping people out until there
is only one person (a very quiet
one!) left reading at the end.

Poetree

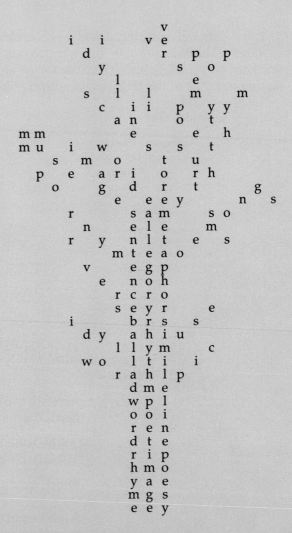

MIKE JOHNSON

Mike Johnson's tree is also a word search puzzle. See how many words connected with poetry you can find in it.

Now create your own 'word search' poem based on the *shape* of your subject. You could try, for example, a poem in the shape of a car, a building, or an animal of some sort.

6S United

An animal arching
A bee biting
A crab croaking
A devil drawing
An elephant ealing
A fox floating
A giraffe grumbling
A horse howling
An insect investigation
A jaw jumping
A kettle kissing
A lion leaping
A mole moving
A newt nursing
An octopus operating
A prince paddling
A queen quivering
A rat rolling
A snake slithering
A tiger tickling
A unicorn urging
A vampire vibrating
A whale whaling
A xylophone exclaiming
A youngster yodelling
A zebra zigging.

CLASS 6S, South Malling CE School

The pattern in this poem is not difficult to work out. 'Alphabet'
poems are easy to write – until you get to 'x'!

Try your own alphabet poem, using different animals. There is a
creature beginning with 'x'; a *xiphias* is a type of swordfish.

3 Poetry patterns 2

A Haiku Yearbook

Snow in January:
Looking for ledges
To hide in unmelted.

February evening:
A cold puddle of petrol
Makes its own rainbow.

Wind in March:
No leaves left
For its stiff summons.

April sunlight:
Even the livid bricks
Muted a little.

Wasp in May:
Storing his venom
For a long summer.

Morning in June:
On the sea's horizon
A white island, alone.

July evening:
Sour reek of beer
Warm by the river.

August morning:
A squirrel leaps and
Only one branch moves.

September chestnuts:
Falling too early,
Split white before birth.

October garden:
At the top of the tree
A thrush stabs an apple.

November morning:
A whiff of cordite
Caught in the leaf mould.

Sun in December:
In his box of straw
The tortoise wakes.

ANTHONY THWAITE

'A Haiku Yearbook' is made up of twelve individual poems called Haiku. The Haiku comes from Japan, but it is now a very popular poetry pattern in many countries and languages.

Some writers on Haiku insist on using a strict pattern of syllables:

5

7

5

Like this one by James Newell:

On a cold morning
The mean frost bites my poor ears
As I walk to school.

Some writers only use the pattern when it suits them.

Try to write a short series of four Haiku. You could write about the seasons, or particular hours of the day.

Make at least one of your Haiku follow the 5 7 5 pattern.

Which 'month' in Anthony Thwaite's poem comes closest to the 5 7 5 pattern?

Four-liners

These short, rhymed poems are intended to be funny, but as the subjects are often gruesome or painful not everyone laughs at them!

Cruel Clever Cat

Sally, having swallowed cheese,
Directs down holes the scented
    breeze,
Enticing thus with baited breath
Nice mice to an untimely death.

GEOFFREY TAYLOR

'There's been an accident,' they said,
'Your servant's cut in half; he's dead!'
'Indeed!' said Mr Jones, 'and please
Send me the half that's got my keys.'

HARRY GRAHAM

FALLING

Auntie, did you feel no pain,
Falling from that apple-tree?
Would you do it, please, again?
'Cos my friend here didn't see.

HARRY GRAHAM

76

JOHN BUN

Here lies John Bun,

He was killed by a gun,

His name was not Bun,

   but Wood,

But Wood would not

rhyme with gun,

   but Bun would.

ANON

Acrostics

Lights of a great city,
Open spaces,
New buildings,
Dangerous traffic
On
Noisy highways.

Cool creature,
Ambulating with his
Tail in the air.

Pour out
Our
E
Motion
S

Wind breathing in its sleep,
Hearing the cat rubbing
Its back on the
Sofa,
Putting your
Ear to a shell,
Running your hands
Softly through sand.

SARA DUNNE

Me

Meghna is my name, but
Everyone calls me Meggie.
Generous is what I am –
    sometimes.
Horrible is what I get –
    sometimes.
Nobody knows my feelings,
And that's how I want to be.

Rather unusual girl you might
    say;
Alone is what I want to be.
Never have I stayed the same,
Absolutely weird is the word for
    me.
MEGHNA RANA

Like her so much, give her a kiss
Over her lips; make her day on
Valentine's day;
End the day with a slap on your
    face!
MAKKU MIAH

Dangerous.
On
Guard.
JANE INCE

Acrostics from Denbigh High
    School, Luton

There are plenty of good subjects for acrostics. You could try:

- your own name
- the place where you live.

Limericks

Limericks have been popular for many years, and many thousands have been written. In all that time, though, no one has been able to write a serious one!

There was an old person in grey,
Whose feelings were tinged with dismay;
She purchased two parrots, and fed them with carrots,
Which pleased that old person in grey.

EDWARD LEAR

There was a young lady of Spain
Who was dreadfully sick in a train,
    Not once, but again,
    And again and again,
And again and again and again.

ANON

There was a young lady called Millicent
Who hated the perfume that Willie sent,
    So she sent it to Liz
    Who declared, 'What a swizz
It's that silly scent Willie sent Millicent!'

ANON

There was a young lady from Tottenham,
Who'd no manners, or else she'd forgotten 'em,
At tea at the vicars,
She tore off her knickers,
Because she said she felt hot in 'em.

ANON

A wonderful bird is the pelican,
His mouth can hold more than his belican,
    He can take in his beak
    Enough food for a week—
I'm damned if I know how the helican.

ANON

Riddles

'Riddles' describe quite ordinary things in such a way that it isn't always easy to guess what is being written about.

Can you answer this question?

This teacher has a white face,
And two hands.
He gives us lots of ticks.
What does he tell us?

Bandit

He has no gun but he still takes your money
You hit him and his silver teeth come rolling out.
He gets angry and takes them all back.
He has bars where no one drinks
Fruit that no one eats.
He's got the biggest pocket you ever saw.
He's got one arm and glowing eyes
That go round and round and round.

CLASS RIDDLE, Sutherland Middle School, Southampton

Keys with no doors,
Hammers with no nails,
Pedals with no bicycle
A noisy zebra!

CLASS RIDDLE, Church of England Middle School, Newport,
Isle of Wight

A   I am a see-through pear
     Hanging from my treeless branch.
     A bit of a conjuror I can ripen suddenly,
     Or disappear at a switch.
     Like the apple I am good for you
     Lengthening your days.

B   I am a small iridescent twig,
     Silver wrapped like a thin sweet.
     A catch-sun, though you will not catch me,
     Too quick as I skim the waters I came from.
     When I pause on a reed or lily's landing pad
     I'm watching you as you marvel.
     You look again: I've gone!

C   Within white seamless walls
     I store my treasure,
     A gold that nourishes.
     Search as you will
     You will find no opening in me.
     Once shattered I'm not for mending.

D   I am at your beginning and your end.
     I dog your footsteps
     And cannot be shaken off.
     Though I fade from view
     You are never alone.
     So silent that you often forget me,
     I am still there,
     Your constant dark spy and companion.

JOHN COTTON

The answers to all these riddles are on page 89.

4 Dialect poems

Turkey Plucking with Grandad

Tha knows what tha wants to do
Get down that garden.
Get them turkeys plucked.
Tha knows I'll crack thee.
Tha wants to come out like a
Snowman tha does.
Tha knows that wing.
Thee bruise it and I'll bruise
Thee tha knows.

SCOTT RICHARDSON

weshin

weyad a coppah int
cornah on ower
scullry
an it wah used
f'rall sortsah
things
weshin (nappies)
boilin (pitsocks)
stewin
boilin pigseds an
ocks an
beehroot

burrah dint like
coppah stick
cos
itwah used
turrit meun
ower Lez wih
more offun un
owt.

BARRY HEATH

chipped

it w'durint war
wen fishshops ad no
paper
an
mimam sent mee for a
basin o'chips
an
a bundle o'wood

Wally Turnbull
from next doower
went wime
an
ont way back
carried bundle o'wood
an
ah carried basin o'chips

wiwent up gennel
an
stopped aht side iz
back doower

ee shahtud 'Catch!'
an
ah dropped basin o'chips
an
caught bundle o'wood.

BARRY HEATH

Writing in dialect is a way of showing the reader how a poem
would sound when read out by a person from a particular region.
You will have heard on television or radio people speaking with a
particular *accent*, such as Scottish, Welsh, Irish or Cockney. It is fun
to try and imitate someone else's accent.

People from different regions often say that they have no accent at
all – it is everyone else that has one!

Dialect is not just an accent. It also includes regional words and
sometimes a 'non-standard' grammar – words are used in a
different way. Barry Heath writes in Nottinghamshire dialect. In
groups, take one of these poems and work out what is happening
in it!

College Learns a Lesson

Look bwoy, lek wi talk.
Sit down na man!
Yuh stan' so tall
is like yuh goin' fall.
Tek a seat an' a drink an' listen.

I neba mean feh cum
ina dis country so long.
Yuh tink me like de col':
yuh tink snow 'ave some kina attraction?

Three years me told me wife,
three years me promise me daughter.
Is twenty years now since me lef de ship
an de only major water I see is when
de gutter don' fall wid de weight o' de rain
by me windo'!

I cum like a sheep wid de res'.
Someone – me na know who –
say it feh deh bes'.
Get a job, buy food, pay de rent
an' sen' home de res' so me wife can save
an' me daughter pray feh de day she too
can cum ina Englan'.

Ten years it take of all I earn
an' now dem here dem wan' to return.
But it not so easy as all of dat
wi three more chil' an' a council flat.
So don' badda ask why me sittin' here
wi me ragged shirt an' two warm beer.
All I had is all I gave.
Remember bwoy, cheap labour
is jus' a slave paid.

CLIVE WEBSTER

Clive Webster writes:

'College Learns a Lesson' is written in the 'Creole' style. 'Creole' is a word we use when talking about ways of speaking that have developed over many years in parts of Africa and the Caribbean. Ever since slavery in Africa, different 'Creole' languages have emerged and for different reasons. Sometimes they would emerge because slaves were forced to forget their own African language and learn the European language of their captors. So, for example, we have Dutch 'Creole', French 'Creole' and English 'Creole'. Sometimes a 'Creole' language would begin because the slaves were taken from different parts of Africa and spoke different languages; to talk to one another, they would make up a new language, a new 'Creole'. This was often very helpful when rebellions were being planned because their captors would not understand what was being said!

I don't think you will have too much difficulty understanding the 'Creole' in this poem. It is similar to the way some people who have come to Britain from the Caribbean speak and can be heard in many towns and cities. In most cases, the words are exactly the same as they are in 'standard English'. In other cases, they are spelt and sound differently. For example, 'never' becomes 'neba'; 'take' becomes 'tek' and 'for' becomes 'feh'. Sometimes two words are used instead of one; so instead of saying 'fallen', the poem says '...don' fall...'.

I wrote this poem because many people I talk to think that everyone who came to Britain from the Caribbean intended to stay for the rest of their lives. Some did, but others didn't. Many had hoped to make enough money to return and live a more comfortable life where they were born. 'College' has also made the mistake of thinking that all Caribbeans came to Britain for good. He is soon put in his place by a much older man who explains just why he's been in England all this time.

Try reading the poem aloud; like a lot of poetry, it is better 'said' than 'read'!

Dahn the Plug-'ole

A muvver was barfin' 'er biby one night,
The youngest of ten and a tiny young mite,
The muvver was pore and the biby was thin,
Only a skelington covered in skin;
The muvver turned rahnd for the soap orf the rack,
She was but a moment, but when she turned back,
The biby was gorn; and in anguish she cried,
'Oh, where is my biby?' – The angels replied:
'Your biby 'as fell dahn the plug-'ole,
 Your biby 'as gorn dahn the plug;
The poor little thing was so skinny and thin
'E oughter been barfed in a jug;
Your biby is perfeckly 'appy,
'E won't need a barf any more,
Your biby 'as fell dahn the plug-ole,
Not lorst, but gorn before.'

ANON

Using the Cockney (London) dialect as featured in this poem, write
a paragraph in which the mother explains to her husband how the
unhappy accident happened.

The Heffalumps

They gorgon on the gridges,
And they bathe in gummy gools,
   They raddle round the rolders
   With their alabaster stools.
They inhabit carawodgities,
In groups of seven or eight,
   And in the sugger seasons,

They attempt to hibernate.
They walk by alliwaddling.
And go for runny trots.
   They cultivate gardenias
   In alabaster pots.
They rallow with the Rurigines,
And wallow in the wough (wuff).
   And muddihydrenate themselves
   With slimy gooly stuff.
They eat the lumptious bumberworm
With honey-bottomed bees
   And drink the gooly waters
   Under harawurly trees.
They greet their friends by horrolling
And make a grooly din.
They scratch their shilly feet
   Against their rinkle-ringy skin.
They shelter under hoolah trees
From splurgipuddling rain
   And when it is uphottening
   They waddle out again.
Their bodies are of greyish hue
With undulating humps,
   They're really quite boristical
   The rhiny heffalumps!

ROSEMARY MARRIOTT

'The Heffalumps' uses a secret language – invented by the poet!
Work out (or make up) meanings for some of the unusual words in
the poem, then try a short 'secret language' poem of your own.

BYE NOW	GOODBYE NOW

BYE NOW

Walk good
  Walk good
Noh mek macca go juk yu
Or cow go buck yu.
Noh mek dog bite yu
Or hungry go ketch yu, yah!

Noh mek sunhot turn yu dry.

Noh mek rain soak yu.
Noh mek tief tief yu
Or stone go buck yu foot, yah!

  Walk good
   Walk good

GOODBYE NOW

Walk well
  Walk well
Don't let thorns run in you
Or let a cow butt you.
Don't let a dog bite you
Or hunger catch you, hear!

Don't let sun's heat turn you
  dry.
Don't let rain soak you.
Don't let a thief rob you
Or a stone bump your foot,
  hear!
  Walk well
   Walk well

JAMES BERRY

Poetry is . . .

. . . what makes you,
Long since buried,
Sneak out of your coffin, out of the graveyard,
To be caught on street corners
Playing exuberantly on a xylophone
You've built from the bones of your skeleton.

LEO AYLEN

Answers to riddles on page 79:
clock
fruit machine
piano

Answers to riddles on page 80:
A light bulb
B dragonfly
C egg
D shadow

Acknowledgements

We are grateful to the following copyright holders for permission to reproduce poetry:

the author, Moira Andrew for 'Missing Person'; the author, Leo Aylen for 'Poetry is . . .' from *Rhymoceros (Macmillan 1989)* © Leo Aylen; the author, Wanda Barford for 'Conversation with an Angel'; Black Sparrow Press for 'This subway station . . .' by Charles Reznikoff from *Poems 1918–1975: The Complete Poems of Charles Reznikoff* © 1976 by Charles Reznikoff; The Bodley Head for 'The Troll' by Thomas Blackburn from *The Devil's Kitchen*; Jonathan Cape Ltd for 'First Day at School' by Roger McGough from *In the Glassroom* & '40-Love' by Roger McGough from *Selected Poems*; Carcanet Press Ltd for 'Opening the Cage' by Edwin Morgan from *Poems of Thirty Years*; the author's agent for 'Ballad of the Faithless Wife' by Charles Causley from *Collected Poems* (Pub. Macmillan); the author, Tony Charles for 'Friend'; the author, John Cotton for his four 'Riddles'; the author, Sue Cowling for 'Freeze'; the author, Hilary Davies for 'The Skateboard Boys' first published in *Wadham College Magazine* 1989; Doubleday, a division of Bantam, Doubleday, Dell Publishing Group Inc for 'Haiku' by Harold G Henderson from *An Introduction to Haiku* © 1958 by Harold G Henderson; the author, Gina Douthwaite for 'The Ice-House' and 'The Good Taste Estate'; Faber and Faber Ltd for 'Then', 'Lines' and 'Fishing Song' from *The Magic Mirror* by Judith Nicholls, 'The Dare', 'Learning to Swim', 'Partners' and 'Advice' from *Midnight Forest* by Judith Nicholls, 'My Parents Kept Me' from *Collected Poems* by Stephen Spender & 'Wish for a Young Wife' by Theodore Roethke from *The Collected Poems of Theodore Roethke*; Grafton Books, a division of the Collins Publishing Group for 'if i have made' by e e cummings from *Complete Poems Volume 1*; Hamish Hamilton Ltd for 'Bye Now' & 'Goodbye Now' by James Berry; the author, Barry Heath for 'weshin' & 'chipped'; the author, Geoffrey Holloway for 'Swot'; the author, Libby Houston for 'Hello there, old stumbling-block!'; the author, Michael Johnson for 'Poetree' from *Poetree* © 1987 Michael Johnson; the author's agent for 'Mixed-Up School' by X J Kennedy from *One Winter Night in August* © 1975 by X J Kennedy; the author, Gerda Mayer for 'At Night in the Laundrette' © 15.4.66 from *The Knockabout Show* (Chatto & Windus 1978); the author's agent for 'Quick on the Draw' by Roger McGough from *Sky in the Pie* pub. Kestrel Books Ltd) & 'Dumb Insolence' by Adrian Mitchell from *Strictly Private* edited by Roger McGough (pub. Penguin Books); the author, Judith Nicholls for 'Dare Cinquains' © Judith Nicholls 1990; the author's agent for 'Scafell Pike' by Norman Nicholson from *Sea to the West* (pub. Faber and Faber); the author, David Orme for 'Acrostics' by Sara Dunne & 'Travelling Man' by Mango Chutney; the author, Joan Poulson for 'Why Won't She Listen?'; the author, Kieran Quigley for 'Black Child'; the author, Irene Rawnsley for 'Down at the Launderette'; Ann Barr, Administratrix Alan Riddell Trust for 'Just a Passing Shower' by Alan Riddell; the Schools Poetry Association for 'The Bed' by Adrian Bowden, 'Turkey Plucking with Grandad' by Scott Richardson, 'Oath of Friendship' by Hayley Young & Acrostics by Meghna Rana, Makku Miah and Jane Ince; James MacGibbon, the executor of the Estate of Stevie Smith for 'The Hound of Ulster' from *The Collected Poems of Stevie Smith* (pub. Penguin Modern Classics); the pupils of Class 6S, South Malling CE School for '6S United'; the author, Sue Stewart for 'I had a secret' & 'I have a friend'; the author, May Swenson for 'Cardinal Ideograms' copyright © 1966 May Swenson in *Poems to Solve*; the author's agent for 'A Haiku Yearbook' by Anthony Thwaite © Anthony Thwaite 1984; University of Queensland Press for 'The Bunyip and the Whistling Kettle' by John Manifold from *Collected Verse* (1978); Unwin Hyman Ltd for 'The wind was on the withered heath' from *The Hobbit* by J R R Tolkien; the author's agent for 'College Learns a Lesson' by Clive Webster; the author, Jim C Wilson for 'Sarah and Teddy'; Hadley Records and Yeldah Music for the lyrics to the song 'Redback on the Toilet Seat' by Slim Newton.

We have unfortunately been unable to trace the copyright holders of 'Script' by Stephen Jenkins, 'The Heffalumps' by Rosemary Marriot & 'How to eat a Poem' by Eve Merriam which appeared in *Enjoying Poetry* and would appreciate any information which would enable us to do so.

We are grateful to the following for permission to reproduce photographs: Judith Nicholls, page 36. Sporting Pictures (UK) Ltd/R. Organ, page 13. Commissioned photographs on pages 25, 51, by John Birdsall.